Flowers

Without a sound the flowers call out.

They shout to insects with their colours,

yellow, red and orange,

blue and pink and white,

"Come here! Come here!

Just here is where you'll

find the nectar."

Baby Birds

Are there baby birds inside the nest yet?

Creep close and listen.

Can you hear tiny little voices calling out?

It's the chicks, with their beaks wide open,

saying feed me, feed me,

feed me.

Growing

The balcony's a jungle, full of plants,
growing food for all the neighbours.

Basil to go on Mr Scarlatti's pizzas,
coriander for Mrs Singh's curries,
mint for Mum's tea when she gets home from
work, lettuce for Dad's sandwiches,

and tomatoes for everyone!

Rainbows

When the sun shines through the rain,
watch out for rainbows!

Sunlight's made of colours –
red, orange, yellow, green, blue, indigo, violet –
all mixed together.

But when sunlight shines through rain,
The raindrops can unmix the colours.
Then ... watch out for rainbows!

7

GEESE

High up, above the roads and the houses,
geese are flying.
They make a wobbly arrow in the sky.

They're going somewhere warmer,
and when they're gone
you know that winter's on its way.

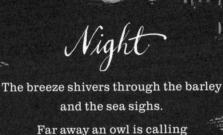

Night

The breeze shivers through the barley
and the sea sighs.

Far away an owl is calling
and a star shines.

The moon sails white and silver
in the dark sky.

Sometimes you can feel
sometimes you can feel
sometimes you can feel the world is turning.

Apples

Fresh from the tree,
the apple sits in your hand,
cool and round,
and streaked with sunset colours.

All around you in the orchard
there are other apples.
Apples grown for juice:
Brown Snout and Harry Masters.

BRAMLEY SEEDLING

Apples grown for cider: Black Dabinett
and Ashton's Bittersweet.

Apples grown for pies:
Hocking's Green and Bramley Seedling.

But the apple in your hand was grown for eating:
George Cave or Dan's Delight,
Honey Pin or Blenheim Orange.
Bite into its crisp, white flesh
and taste the sweetness.

BLACK DABINETT

BLENHEIM ORANGE

Spiderlings

What left this sea of silver
That shines and shakes,
As if the breeze was ruffling the surface of a lake?

It's simply spider silk –
A million tiny strings,
The silken parachutes of baby spiderlings.

Feather

I found a feather on the ground.
It looked so sad and scruffy
split into little spiky barbs.

I pulled it tight between my fingers,
the way a bird does with its beak;
the stringy barbs zipped back together,
to make the feather whole again.

Then I swooshed it through the air
and I could feel it trying to fly.

WINTER TREES

Winter trees are naked.
All their leaves are gone.
You can see their trunks,
some smooth and straight,
some bent and wrinkled.
You can see the way
some branches
dip down to the ground
and some reach up high.
And you can see
the criss-cross patterns
that the twigs make
against the sky.